11+ English Spelling & Vocabulary

Advanced Level
WORKBOOK 9

Dr Stephen C Curran

with Warren Vokes

Edited by Mark Schofield

This book belongs to

ae TUITION

Accelerated Education Publications Ltd.

loan	coax	oath
active	action	preserve
prepare	compare	beware
betray	fortunate	unfortunate

Exercise 184a

1) He caught just a brief **glimpse** of her face in the crowd.

2) The sign read ' _____ of the Dog!' but the dog looked very docile.

3) A sudden gust caught the sails but his swift _____ prevented a capsizal.

4) She offered a lettuce leaf to the timid rabbit to _____ it out of the hutch.

5) She has great natural ability and shows great _____ as a future champion.

6) The children's parents had instilled in them a _____ of right and wrong.

7) It was judged to be an _____ accident and no one was held responsible.

8) It is difficult to _____ the abilities of sportsmen from different eras.

9) She asked the bank for a _____ to enable her to buy a new car.

10) "Stop crying, take a deep breath and _____ yourself."   Score [/ 10]

Exercise 184b

11) It is difficult to _____ the cost of the damage but it is considerable.

12) She tried to stay calm but she knew her bright eyes would _____ her excitement.

13) It was a complex case, so they engaged a solicitor to _____ them.

14) Our MP played a very _____ part in opposing the closure of the Post Office.

15) The witness held the Bible in his hand and recited the _____ on the card.

16) Her great _____ was apparent when her father came home on leave.

17) The policemen told the youths to _____ their noisy behaviour.

18) "Consider yourself _____ that I am letting you off with just a warning!"

19) The council is very keen to _____ the area's rural character.

20) The captain told the cabin crew to _____ for take-off.   Score [/ 10]

ae

Word Bank

moderate   estimate
happiness   compose
advise   promise
glimpse   sense

Word Bank TOTAL 3,680

Across

184

2. Something that somebody does.
4. To keep something protected and make sure it lasts.
6. Money lent to somebody.
9. Enjoying good luck.
12. Moving about, working, or doing something.
14. To harm or be disloyal to your own country or another person by helping or giving information to an enemy.
15. To make something ready for use or action.
17. Feeling or showing pleasure, contentment, or joy.
18. A quick or incomplete sighting.

Down

1. Not large, great, or severe.
3. Never experiencing good luck.
4. To assure somebody that something will certainly happen or be done.
5. To make an approximate calculation.
7. A formal or legally binding promise.
8. To make something by combining together.
10. The ability to make intelligent decisions or sound judgments.
11. To examine two or more people or things for similarities or differences.
13. To gently persuade somebody to do something.
14. To be on guard against.
16. To suggest or recommend a course of action to somebody.

Put the mystery letter (✳) into the box marked **184** below. Add in the mystery letters from puzzles **185** to **190** then rearrange them to make **Kate's Mystery Word**.

The clue is **PET**.

Crossword grid: 2 Across = A C T I O N

184	185	186	187	188	189	190

Now rearrange them:

Mystery Word:

Score / 20

3

wrestle	wrist	written
gentlemen	heathen	beggar
cellar	pillar	grammar
burglar	produce	promote

Across

185

5. Someone who enters a building illegally, usually in order to steal something.
6. To raise somebody to a more senior job or a higher position or rank.
9. A large North American bird that is raised as poultry.
10. A series of musical notes that make a simple melody.
11. An underground room that is usually used for storage.
14. Any long, hollow cylinder used to transport or store liquids.
15. To fight by gripping and pushing.
16. Past participle of *'write'*.
17. Used as a polite term to refer to men.

Down

1. A vertical column that is part of a building and can be used for support or decoration.
2. The system of rules by which words are formed and put together to make sentences.
3. The joint at the base of the hand.
4. To make or create something.
5. Somebody who begs for money or food from strangers.
6. To have or own something.
7. As a whole, from beginning to end, or including everything.
8. To develop or advance continuously.
11. A structure for venting gas, smoke or steam from a fire or furnace.
12. An offensive term that deliberately insults somebody who does not acknowledge the God of the Bible, Torah or Koran.
13. Clothes worn during a specific period of time or in a specific location.

Mystery Letter

Score

/20

progress	possess
entire	chimney
turkey	tune
tube	costume

Word Bank
TOTAL
3,700

Exercise 185a

1) He disturbed the _____ who had broken into his house.

2) He managed to _____ him to the ground and hold him until the police arrived.

3) He was led away handcuffed to the policeman's _____ .

4) Despite many hours in negotiations, they had made very little _____ .

5) America celebrates Thanksgiving Day with a _____ dinner.

6) The dress rehearsal, with all the actors in full _____ , went very well.

7) The _____ 's Opera is a vivid depiction of London lowlife in the 18th century.

8) The headmaster of the village school is a prominent _____ of the community.

9) She used a rubber patch to repair the puncture in the inner _____ .

10) The company distributed flyers to _____ its services. **Score** ⬚ 10

Exercise 185b

11) She had _____ a long letter of complaint and sent it to the airline.

12) Missionaries attempted to convert the _____ natives to Christianity.

13) A wide variety of _____ can be bought at the farmers' market.

14) He is an ardent collector with a desire to _____ many fine works of art.

15) The _____ under the house was cold and damp with a musty smell.

16) The singer was off-key and could not sing in _____ with the band.

17) They shook hands and made a _____ 's agreement.

18) Thick black smoke belched from the _____ , polluting the atmosphere.

19) The day was a complete fiasco and an _____ waste of time.

20) "Your _____ is appalling! It's 'haven't', not 'ain't'!" **Score** ⬚ 10

5

discontent	**represent**	**evident**
frequent	**accident**	**grocer**
groceries	**tempt**	**attempt**
temptation	**mention**	**attention**

Exercise 186a

1) Blue lines on a map are used to _____ rivers and streams.

2) He managed to _____ his way through and get to the front of the crowd.

3) She deemed it unwise to _____ her involvement in the company's failure.

4) My grandfather was a _____ and his shop sold food from dawn till dusk.

5) He was unhappy and he registered his _____ in a letter to the company.

6) He addressed the letter for the _____ of the company director.

7) The fire was thought to have been caused by the _____ flame of a candle.

8) The full extent of her injuries did not become _____ until they tried to move her.

9) She succumbed to _____ and ate one more chocolate.

10) The farmer put out the cows to _____ in the top pasture.   **Score** ⬚ 10

Exercise 186b

11) It is a very tense and difficult _____ that requires tact and diplomacy.

12) The advertisement was designed to _____ people to buy the new chocolate bar.

13) She loaded her shopping trolley with enough _____ to last a month.

14) It was a _____ remarkable achievement for her to win three Olympic gold medals.

15) In his acceptance _____ he thanked all those who had voted for him.

16) He was a _____ visitor to the museum: he spent every free day there.

17) She failed on her third _____ and had to withdraw from the contest.

18) It is a very grand _____ , printed on a thick card with a gold deckle edge.

19) She was injured in a riding _____ : her horse bolted.

20) A child needs protein for healthy _____ .   **Score** ⬚ 10

Word Bank TOTAL 3,720

Across

186

3. Unhappiness or dissatisfaction.
5. The joint between the upper and lower parts of the human arm.
6. Somebody who owns or runs a shop selling food and other household goods.
7. Honestly, without affectation or pretence.
8. To touch against the surface of something lightly in passing.
10. The general conditions that prevail in a place or society.
12. The ability to speak.

Across (continued)

14. A craving or desire for something, especially something thought wrong.
16. The way things happen without any planning, apparent cause, or deliberate intent.
18. To act or speak on behalf of somebody or something.
19. The process of becoming larger and more mature through natural development.
20. Mental focus, serious consideration, or concentration.

Down

1. Goods, especially food, sold in a grocer's shop.
2. To go to or be in a place often.
4. To use a particular word or name when speaking or writing, often in a casual way.
9. Easy to see or clear to see or understand.
11. An offer to come or go somewhere, or the making of such an offer.
13. An act of trying to do something.
15. Not covered by clothing.
17. To cause desire or craving to rise in somebody.

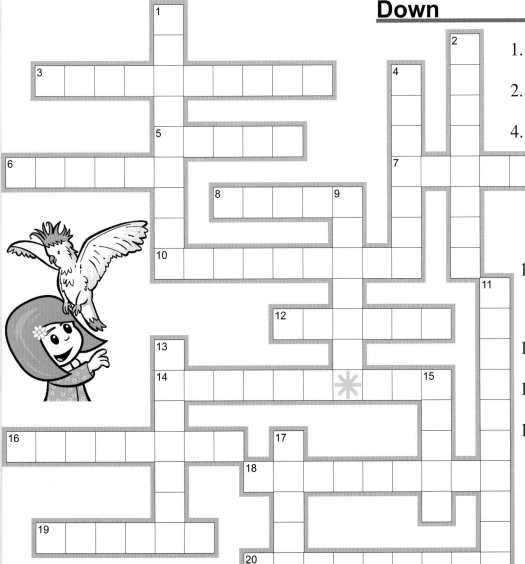

Mystery Letter [ ]

Score [/ 20]

accept   according   plunge
population   satin   honour
harbour   habit   pigeon
gulf   labour   devour

Across

187

5. Not under the influence of alcohol.
6. A small, simple house, especially one made of wood in forest or mountain areas.
7. A reward or punishment that is given in return for something.
8. Acting, moving, or happening very quickly.
10. A large inlet of a sea similar to a bay but often longer and more enclosed by land.
15. Being in agreement or coming to an agreement.
16. Work done using the strength of the body.
17. A medium-sized bird commonly trained for racing or carrying messages.
18. Fairness or reasonableness, especially in the way people are treated or decisions are made.

Down

1. A habit, custom, or usual way of doing something.
2. An action or behaviour pattern that is regular, repetitive, and often unconscious.
3. To have or show great respect and admiration for somebody or something.
4. To take something that is offered.
5. A fabric woven of silk or rayon with a smooth glossy finish and a dull back.
7. The total number of people who inhabit an area, region or country.
9. Work done by somebody for somebody else as a job, a duty, a punishment, or a favour.
11. To eat something quickly and hungrily.
12. An open metal, ceramic, or plastic container with sloping sides, typically used for holding water or washing.
13. To provide somebody with shelter or sanctuary.
14. To move, rush, dive, or be thrown suddenly downwards or forwards.

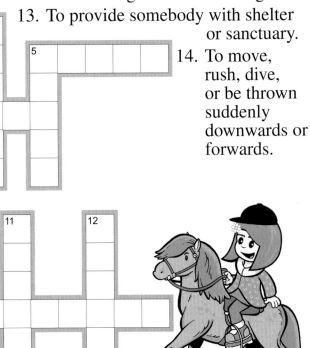

Mystery Letter

Score

20

Exercise 187a

1) "The children _____ in minutes what it's taken you all afternoon to cook!"

2) There was a _____ change in the company's fortunes: boom to bust in just weeks.

3) The sudden storm forced the fishing fleet to return to _____ .

4) They could not agree: the _____ between them was just too wide.

5) He saw the car skid off the mountain road and _____ into the river below.

6) They decided against matt or gloss finish and chose instead a _____ paint.

7) The idea is fine in theory, but in _____ it may not be possible.

8) A _____ and rational assessment of the probable outcome was needed.

9) The _____ is drained by the river and its tributaries which flow into a vast lake.

10) He booked his car in for a _____ at the local garage.   **Score** ◻ 10

Exercise 187b

11) The increase in a country's _____ puts a strain on its resources.

12) She fell ill on the cruise and retired to her _____ to rest and recover.

13) The monk wore a brown, hooded _____ fastened at the waist with a cord.

14) The invoice was due for _____ on the last day of the month.

15) "Her poor exam results don't do _____ to her true ability."

16) A _____ carried a message from the trenches to army headquarters.

17) He assembled the kit exactly _____ to the instructions.

18) "I understand your concern: there's no need to _____ the point."

19) Her achievement is an _____ to both the school and her parents.

20) "I _____ your apology and now consider the matter closed." **Score** ◻ 10

9

excite	exciting	excellent
exclaim	exclaimed	construct
contribute	consume	confirm
contrast	explore	exploration

Exercise 188a

1) She rang to ask if he would _____ to her charity appeal.

2) The school's results were _____ and exceeded all expectations.

3) They won fairly and squarely and it is churlish to _____ them their success.

4) "I'm waiting for an _____ from you and it had better be a good one!"

5) The match was very _____ with neither side gaining the upper hand.

6) She asked for his help and he was happy to _____ .

7) The luxury enjoyed above decks on the *Titanic* was in stark _____ to steerage.

8) Oil _____ becomes more expensive and less fruitful as supplies diminish.

9) Fans _____ air under pressure from outlets under a hovercraft's apron.

10) Not every _____ that an inventor has comes to fruition.

Score ☐ 10

Exercise 188b

11) "I'm rich!" he _____ , when he checked his lottery numbers.

12) She told her son not to _____ the dog because it might bite.

13) She tried not to step on the cracks as she walked along the _____ .

14) "How did ancient civilisations manage to _____ such wondrous buildings?"

15) The forest fire blazed out of control and seemed to _____ everything in its path.

16) It was a special occasion and they dined in _____ at a top London restaurant.

17) He had not intended to _____ so loudly: now everyone was looking at him.

18) She fell into the nettles and an _____ rash appeared on her bare arms and legs.

19) He told the committee to _____ all possible avenues of research.

20) He asked the hotel to _____ his booking in writing.

Score ☐ 10

explanation	style
pavement	expel
angry	envy
idea	oblige

Word Bank TOTAL 3,760

Across

188

1. To do or give something along with others, that helps to achieve a specific purpose or goal.
3. The resentful or unhappy feeling of wanting somebody else's success, good fortune, qualities, or possessions.
5. A personal opinion or belief.
6. Of a very high quality or standard.
7. To travel to a place to discover what it is like or what is there.
10. A statement giving reasons for something or details of something.
12. Past participle of 'exclaim'.
13. To speak or cry out loudly and suddenly.

Across (continued)

16. The difference between the lightest and the darkest parts of something.
17. A distinctive and identifiable form in an artistic medium such as music, architecture or literature.

Down

1. To prove to be true and valid.
2. To push or drive something out with force.
3. To cause somebody to feel enjoyment or pleasurable anticipation.
4. To build or assemble something by putting together separate parts in an ordered way.
6. The testing of a number of places for natural resources.
8. Causing feelings of happiness and enthusiasm or nervousness and tension.
9. A paved path for pedestrians alongside a street.
11. To bind somebody morally or legally to do something.
14. To eat or drink something, especially in large amounts.
15. Feeling extremely annoyed, often about an insult or a wrong.

Mystery Letter

Score

20

11

height   **either**   **neither**
reign   **foreign**   **junior**
language   **monument**   **department**
swear   **gospel**   **compel**

Across

1. Somebody who lives or is located very close by.
3. Relating to youth, childhood, or children.
5. A place in a hospital, prison or other institution, or in a large house, consecrated for Christian worship.
9. A precious stone such as a diamond or a sapphire.
10. To use blasphemous or obscene language.
14. A large stone statue or carving designed and built as a lasting public tribute to a person, a group of people, or an event.
15. The distance between the lowest point and the highest point.
16. A unit of dry or liquid measure in the British Imperial system, equal to 8 imperial gallons.

Across (continued)

18. Any of the blood vessels that carry blood to the heart.
19. Relating to, from, or located in, another country or countries other than your own.

Down

1. Used preceding two alternatives joined by 'nor' to indicate that both did not happen or are not true.
2. One or more things wrapped up together in paper or other packaging.
4. A set of beliefs held strongly by a group or person.
6. The speech of a country, region, or group of people.
7. To force somebody to do something.
8. A specialised section of a large organisation such as a university or store.
11. One or the other when it does not matter which.
12. The progression or development of a sequence of events.
13. A length of fabric, usually sheer, worn by a woman over the head and face as a concealment or for protection.
17. The period of time during which somebody, especially a king or queen, rules a nation.

Mystery Letter

Score
/ 20

12

Exercise 189a

1) Human nature resists the attempts of others to _____ one to act in a certain way.

2) The estate was divided into smaller plots and each _____ of land was sold off.

3) The Cenotaph in Whitehall is a _____ to those killed in battle.

4) Evangelical _____ music was a strong influence in the development of soul music.

5) "She kept her light hidden under a _____ : I never realised she had such talent!"

6) For 25 years *Concorde* was the _____ in the crown of British Airways's fleet.

7) The _____ of Queen Elizabeth I lasted from 1558 until her death in 1603.

8) "It was the _____ of folly to go on alone: you should have waited for me!"

9) They discovered a rich _____ of ore and proceeded to extract it.

10) The young girl took the _____ and began her life in the convent.

Score / 10

Exercise 189b

11) He and his _____ shared the cost of the new fence between their gardens.

12) "I _____ that I shall tell the truth, the whole truth, and nothing but the truth."

13) He joined the Cabinet as a _____ minister, but was destined for higher office.

14) Her body lay in the _____ of rest at the undertakers' until her funeral.

15) "What do you want for supper? You can have _____ spaghetti or pasta."

16) She attended a six week introductory _____ in genealogy at the local college.

17) These outbursts are out of character and completely _____ to her nature.

18) BASIC, C++ and Pascal are examples of computer programming _____ .

19) The huge _____ store could supply almost everything.

20) _____ of the boys wants to go on the fishing trip.

Score / 10

supply	support	attract
arrest	shrink	avenue
diamond	foundation	fuel
cruelly	government	madam

Exercise 190a

1) It was a case of wrongful _____ and he was released without charge.

2) The _____ is injected and the X-ray will indicate any blockages in the arteries.

3) "Can I be of assistance _____ and show you some evening dresses?"

4) His car was low on _____ and he needed to find a petrol station soon.

5) They had a plentiful _____ of food and water: enough for several days.

6) Her's was judged to be the winning _____ and she was awarded first prize.

7) She rises to a challenge and does not _____ from tackling tough problems.

8) The nurse removed the _____ , cleaned the wound and applied a new dressing.

9) He could not follow suit with a _____ , so he had to pick up a card.

10) "You'll _____ your life unless you mend your ways."

Score ⬛ 10

Exercise 190b

11) His passport was sent under _____ cover as a security measure.

12) He had to _____ his birth certificate with his application.

13) The Queen's Speech sets out her _____ 's legislative programme.

14) The conjurer waved his _____ wand and completed the trick.

15) The children worked hard to raise money to _____ their local charity.

16) All the usual methods had failed and a new _____ of enquiry was needed.

17) The mayor laid the _____ stone at the start of the building's construction.

18) Their _____ was blocked by a fallen tree and they had to turn back.

19) Her injury _____ dashed all hopes of competing in the Olympics.

20) The hotel lowered its prices to _____ more guests.

Score ⬛ 10

Word Bank

passage	**bandage**
separate	**enclose**
entry	**magic**
dye	**ruin**

Word Bank TOTAL 3,800

Across

190

2. The basis for something, for example a theory or an idea.
5. A corridor or an outdoor path enclosed on both sides.
7. A long, narrow strip of fabric for covering an injury.
9. A supposed supernatural power that makes impossible things happen.
12. Deliberately and remorselessly causing pain or anguish.
14. To surround something or shut something in.

Across (continued)

16. The physical remains of something such as a building or city that has decayed or been destroyed.
17. To draw objects nearer, for example as a magnet draws iron objects towards it.
18. To keep something or somebody upright or in place, or prevent something or somebody from falling.

Down

1. To give, sell, or make available.
2. Something that is burned to provide power or heat.
3. A road lined with trees.
4. A polite term of address for a woman, especially a customer in a shop, restaurant or hotel.
6. To become smaller or cause something to become smaller.
8. A group of people who have the power to make and enforce laws for a country or area.
10. To take somebody into custody on suspicion of having committed a crime.
11. To colour or stain something by soaking it in a colouring solution.
13. Not touching or connected, or not in the same place.
14. A way into a place.
15. A transparent form of carbon that is the hardest known mineral and the most highly prized gemstone.

! Don't forget to go back to page **3** and complete **Kate's Mystery Word**.

Score

Mystery Letter

 /20

15

At the Police Station

Can you find all these words in the picture below? Write the correct word against each number.

baton	constable	lamp	whistle	radio
handcuffs	helmet	epaulette	key	motorcycle
torch	patrol car	sergeant	poster	notebook

1._____ 2._____ 3._____

4._____ 5._____ 6._____

7._____ 8._____ 9._____

10._____ 11._____ 12._____

13._____ 14._____ 15._____

At the Greengrocer's

Can you find all these words in the picture below? Write the correct word against each number. When you have finished you can colour in the picture if you want to.

trug	melon	punnet	price tag	awning
sack	potatoes	money bag	umbrella	container
apron	besom	scales	carrots	spring balance

1._____ 　 2._____ 　 3._____

4._____ 　 5._____ 　 6._____

7._____ 　 8._____ 　 9._____

10._____ 　 11._____ 　 12._____

13._____ 　 14._____ 　 15._____

latitude	altitude	minute
reduce	refuge	employ
employer	custom	customer
fever	observe	observation

Across

1. Made or built to order.
4. Very hard work for very low pay.
6. To leave or abandon a place or a person.
7. A vegetable in the form of a rounded edible bulb with hard pungent flesh.
9. A general office worker.
11. To give paid work to somebody.
12. Extremely small in size or scope.
16. A person or group that engages workers.
17. An abnormally high body temperature.
18. The height of something above sea level.
19. To watch attentively.

Down

2. A serious lack of happiness.
3. An imaginary line joining points around the Earth's surface.
5. A low-growing perennial plant with irregular purplish blue flowers.
8. A musical instrument with four strings, held under the chin and played with a bow.
9. A person or company who buys goods or services.
10. The attentive watching of somebody or something.
13. To become or make something smaller in size, number, extent, degree, or intensity.
14. A leaping insect that has biting mouthparts, long legs and antennae.
15. A sheltered or protected state safe from something threatening, harmful, or unpleasant.

Put the mystery letter (✳) into the box marked **191** below. Add in the mystery letters from puzzles **192** to **198** then rearrange them to make **Dickens's Mystery Word**.
The clue is **GARDENING**.

Enter your mystery letters here:

191	192	193	194	195	196	197	198

Now rearrange them:

Mystery Word:

Score
20

desert	slavery
misery	violin
violet	cricket
clerk	onion

Exercise 191a

1) "It's a very creative job, allowing me a great deal of _____ ."

2) He was kept in hospital overnight for _____ .

3) He asked the _____ of the works to visit the site and inspect the building work.

4) The heavy rain obscured his vision and he was forced to _____ speed.

5) The American Republican party was formed in 1856 to oppose _____ .

6) Antonio Stradivari is arguably the most famous _____ maker in history.

7) He peeled the _____ under running water to prevent his eyes from streaming.

8) The company is a good _____ , providing an excellent salary and a pension.

9) He rang his _____ to tell her the order was ready for collection.

10) They scored the winning goal in the last _____ of play. **Score** ⬛ 10

Exercise 191b

11) The excitement reached _____ pitch and the tension was unbearable.

12) Her youngest daughter gave her an African _____ in a pot for Mother's Day.

13) The vet suggested that it would be kinder to put the animal out of its _____ .

14) The _____ match ended with the home team winning by three wickets.

15) It is customary to _____ a two minute silence at 11 o'clock on Armistice Day.

16) It was necessary to _____ extra staff to meet the demand for their product.

17) The _____ was blisteringly hot during the day and very cold by night.

18) It is an ancient _____ that has been handed down from father to son.

19) They sought _____ on higher ground to escape the flood waters.

20) "We shall be cruising at an _____ of 30,000 feet." **Score** ⬛ 10

common	**collect**	**connect**
connection	**command**	**errand**
funnel	**flannel**	**channel**
current	**arrange**	**arranging**

Exercise 192a

1) A luxurious cabin _____ was moored in the marina.

2) It was a _____ question to answer without upsetting anyone.

3) He was busily _____ the paintings to be displayed in the exhibition.

4) The ship's _____ belched smoke as the crew stoked the boilers to raise steam.

5) The poor animal had suffered _____ but was rescued by the RSPCA.

6) She missed her _____ and had to wait for a later train.

7) It was a strong _____ with a dangerous undertow.

8) He had played the _____ so many times, it was difficult to be cast as the hero.

9) The peacekeeping force was acting under the _____ of the United Nations.

10) He gave the _____ and the barrage commenced.   **Score** ⬛ 10

Exercise 192b

11) "I can't prove it, but I _____ that you are up to no good!"

12) She offered to _____ her parents from the airport on their return.

13) He opened an art _____ and invited artists and sculptors to display their work.

14) The _____ fired a 21-gun salute on the monarch's birthday.

15) He managed to _____ the two wires and complete the circuit.

16) He was sent on an _____ to collect her suit from the dry-cleaners.

17) Their coach told them to _____ all their energies into winning the game.

18) People use the _____ for exercise, to walk their dogs, or just for recreation.

19) She used a wet _____ to wash her child's face and hands.

20) "I would like to _____ a meeting for later this week."   **Score** ⬛ 10

gallery	difficult
umbrella	neglect
cruiser	suspect
villain	cannon

Across

192

1. A communication link, especially between telephones.
4. A short trip somewhere to do something on behalf of somebody else.
6. A weapon used in former times to fire heavy iron balls and other projectiles.
7. Requiring a lot of planning or effort to accomplish.
9. A wide passage of water between an island and a larger body of land.
13. Doing what is necessary to make something happen in the future.
15. A soft cotton cloth with a nap on one side.

Across (continued)

16. To gather things and bring them together.
17. To doubt the truth or validity of something.

Down

1. Belonging to, or shared by, two or more people or groups.
2. An order or instruction given by somebody in authority.
3. To fail to give the proper or required care and attention to somebody or something.
5. A fast, easily manoeuvrable, warship.
8. A collapsible canopy held in the hand to protect somebody from rain.
9. The steady flow of water or air in a particular direction.
10. To link or join two or more parts, things, or people together.
11. To move or direct something into and through a narrow space.
12. An evil character in a novel, film, play, or other story.
13. To put people or things in a position or order.
14. A balcony or passage running along the wall of a large building.

Mystery Letter **Score** /20

21

argue	argument	valuable
vegetable	comfortable	citizen
century	centre	central
hospital	surpass	purchase

Across

193

3. To, or at, a point that is more distant in place or time.

5. To scrape or make a slight mark in the surface of something.

7. In, near, or forming the middle of something.

9. A member of the clergy of a Christian, especially Protestant, church.

12. To take or accept something given.

14. To express disagreement with somebody, especially continuously or angrily.

15. The whole of somebody's property, possessions and capital.

16. Any period of a hundred years.

18. A reason put forward in support of a point of view.

19. Making somebody feel physically relaxed.

20. To mislead somebody or hide the truth deliberately.

Down

1. Worth a great deal of money.

2. The middle point, area, or part of something that is the same distance from all edges or opposite sides.

4. Any plant with edible parts, especially leafy or fleshy parts that are used mainly for soups and salads and to accompany main courses.

6. Having every necessary part or everything that is wanted.

8. To buy something using money or its equivalent.

10. To go beyond what was expected or hoped for.

Down (continued)

11. An institution where people receive medical, surgical, or psychiatric treatment and nursing care.

13. Somebody who has the legal right to live in a country.

17. The reason for which something exists or for which it has been done or made.

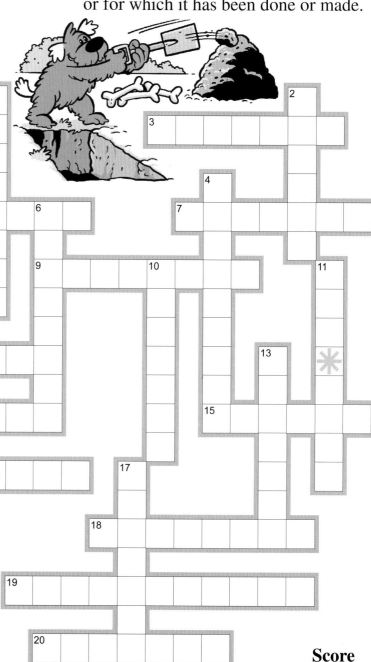

Mystery Letter

Score
20

purpose	further
scratch	complete
estate	minister
receive	deceive

Exercise 193a

1) At last he found the final item and could _____ the collection.

2) A member of the crew was sick, so they had to _____ from the event.

3) A new _____ would provide improved heath care for the community.

4) They engaged in a vehement _____ and almost came to blows.

5) The children succeeded in finding their way to the _____ of the maze.

6) Although a member of the Cabinet, he is a _____ without portfolio.

7) The spectators stood and applauded when the batsman scored a _____ .

8) Olive, rapeseed, sesame and sunflower oils are all _____ oils.

9) They planned to _____ the opposition with diversionary tactics.

10) It is a _____ necklace, insured for thousands of pounds.

Score ◿ 10

Exercise 193b

11) Her examination results _____ even her most optimistic expectations.

12) He emigrated and, after a few years, he applied to become an Australian _____ .

13) He made _____ inquiries and discovered that there had been a mistake.

14) The probate court dealt with the administration of the deceased's _____ .

15) Each denied the other's point of view and they continued to _____ the toss.

16) "They're not what you'd call well-off, but they're certainly _____ ."

17) She went to the palace with her family to _____ the OBE.

18) The _____ heating broke down and the children were sent home from school.

19) It was no accident: he had broken the window on _____ .

20) "I'd like to _____ a book token for my son."

Score ◿ 10

scare	scarce	scarf
meanness	straight	insane
invade	inspire	include
introduce	entrance	performance

Exercise 194a

1) "You two are giving me a _____ with your constant bickering."

2) A dowser was employed to _____ for underground water.

3) The document contained nothing of _____ and was worthless.

4) She wrapped her _____ around her neck and put on her gloves.

5) It is an impressive _____ with a pair of huge ornate wrought iron gates.

6) Studying great artists' work would _____ him to paint.

7) The psychiatrist pronounced her _____ and she was sectioned.

8) Dickens's miserly character, Scrooge, personifies _____ .

9) After the _____ , they went backstage to meet the cast.

10) She went _____ home after the party ended.

Score ☐ 10

Exercise 194b

11) It is said that _____ never strikes twice in the same place.

12) He clapped his hands loudly to _____ away the nearby pigeons.

13) The boxer moved to his left to _____ his opponent's punch.

14) She forgot to _____ a tip when she paid her bill.

15) His back continued to _____ for days after he strained it.

16) Wars often begin with a politician's decision to _____ another country.

17) Viewers were invited to telephone and _____ a donation to the appeal.

18) She waited for her husband to _____ her to his colleagues.

19) He checked the account _____ on his bank statement.

20) Money was _____ and they had to economise.

Score ☐ 10

Word Bank TOTAL 3,880

Across

194

3. A solemn promise or vow.
6. To hold somebody's attention and produce a sense of wonder in that person.
7. Having a godlike nature.
9. Without bends, curves, irregularities, or deviations.
12. Being in insufficient supply.
14. To encourage people into greater efforts, or greater enthusiasm, or creativity.
17. A particular kind of matter or material.
19. A pain in the head.

Down

1. Unkindness, maliciousness, or unwillingness to spend money on other people.
2. To move quickly and suddenly to one side to avoid being caught or hit.
4. Flashes of light seen in the sky, usually occurring during a thunderstorm.
5. A presentation of an artistic work to an audience, for example a play or piece of music.
8. To achieve or maintain a position of steadiness while resting on a narrow base.
10. To present yourself or another person to somebody else and become acquainted with that person.
11. To feel, or be the site of, a dull constant pain.
13. To enter and spread through something completely.
14. Legally incompetent or irresponsible because of a psychiatric disorder.

Down (continued)

15. A piece of cloth worn around the neck.
16. To make somebody or something part of a group.
18. To make somebody afraid or alarmed.

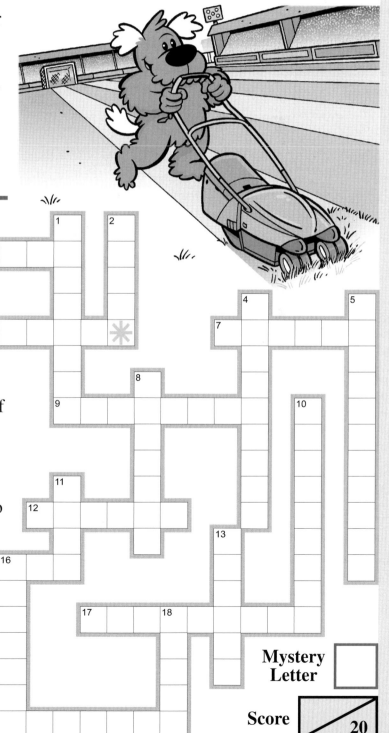

Mystery Letter

Score 20

Oliver's
Page of Knowledge
Conveyances and Components

Hovercraft (7)
Clue: The flap, or apron, around the bottom of a hovercraft that allows it to travel over land and water supported by a cushion of air that it creates by blowing air downwards.

Freighter (2)
Clue: A simple crane, named after a London hangman who was working at Tyburn in the early 17th century, that is often used for lifting cargo off or onto a ship.

Aeroplane (5)
Clue: An aerofoil, usually on the tail of an aeroplane, that pivots vertically and controls left-to-right movement.

Airboat (10)
Clue: A revolving shaft with spiral blades that causes the swamp boat to move by the backward thrust of air.

Skiff (3)
Clue: A more or less U-shaped pivoting metal rest fitted to the side of a rowing boat, in which an oar rests.

Conveyance		Component
1. _____	with	_____
2. _____	with	_____
3. _____	with	_____
4. _____	with	_____
5. _____	with	_____

ae

**Rudder · Tender
Rotor · Skirt · Propeller
Rowlock · Chain · Derrick
Ramp · Rigging**

"Link the name of the conveyance with its component in the answers below."

Pantechnicon
Clue: Attached to the rear, supported by hinges, it is lowered to provide easy access for loading and unloading.

1

Galleon
Clue: An intricate web of ropes, wires and pulleys that support the mast and control the sails of a boat.

8

Steam Engine
Clue: The permanently coupled rear part of a large steam locomotive which carries its coal and water.

4

Bicycle
Clue: A flexible interlinked series of metal links that engage with sprockets to transfer the power, generated by pedalling, to the rear wheel.

9

Helicopter
Clue: An assembly of aerofoils that rotates about a hub to give lift to an aircraft and, once airborne, to propel it through the air.

6

Conveyance   Component

6. _____ with _____

7. _____ with _____

8. _____ with _____

9. _____ with _____

10. _____ with _____

adopt	prompt	cupboard
sponge	problem	guard
guess	guinea	tongue
rogue	decide	recite

Exercise 195a

1) Her horse was _____ so she stopped to let it drink at the stream.

2) He is a lovable _____ despite his irrepressible urge to do mischief.

3) They wore protective suits to _____ against contamination.

4) All the members of the group worked together in _____ to achieve their goal.

5) The Nile valley is very _____ due to the river flooding and depositing alluvium.

6) She always tries to follow _____ and wear the latest style of clothes.

7) She tried to _____ the answer but she was hopelessly wrong.

8) Her father built a run so that her pet _____ pig could be put out on the lawn.

9) The actor forgot his line and the _____ called it out for him.

10) "If I _____ five by four I get twenty."

Score 10

Exercise 195b

11) He preferred to _____ off others and made no attempt to earn a living.

12) "We need more information before we can _____ on a course of action."

13) The teacher asked her to come to the front of the class and _____ the poem.

14) It is a monumental task to _____ a country's people following a civil war.

15) My little brother opens _____ doors and removes the contents.

16) It was her _____ birthday and she blew out all nine candles with one breath.

17) He was a _____ child and often in trouble with the authorities.

18) The local party decided to _____ the younger man as their candidate.

19) It was a _____ that more were not injured in the accident.

20) He pulled up the _____ and tied his shoelace.

Score 10

concert	fertile
unite	mercy
multiply	ninth
fashion	thirsty

Across

195

3. To bring things together or come together to form or act as a unit.
7. To read something aloud or repeat something from memory.
9. Done at once and without delay.
11. To protect somebody or something against danger or loss.
13. A piece of furniture, or a small room, used for storing food and other kitchen necessities.
14. The style of dress, behaviour, way of living, or other expression that is popular at present.
15. Feeling the need to drink a liquid.
16. A gold coin worth 21 shillings that was a British unit of currency between 1663 and 1813.
18. A difficult situation, matter, or person.
19. To increase, or make something increase, by a considerable amount, or degree.

Down

1. Somebody who is unscrupulous or dishonest, especially someone who is nevertheless likable.
2. Kindness or forgiveness shown to an offender or to somebody a person has power over.
4. One of nine equal parts of something.
5. A lightweight, porous, absorbent, natural or synthetic material used for bathing or cleaning.
6. The movable fleshy organ inside the mouth.
8. A public musical performance.
10. Capable of breeding or reproducing.
12. To make a choice or come to a conclusion about something.
16. To form an opinion about something without enough evidence to make a definite judgment.
17. To legally raise another's child as your own.

Mystery Letter

Score /20

archery	arguing	emphasising
kilogram	empress	laundrette
guitars	encounter	anthology
cardigan	choreographer	hexagon

Across

196

2. An aircraft without wings that moves by means of a rotor that spins round above it.

5. A person who plans out the movements that dancers are to make to a piece of music.

9. A two-dimensional figure that has six sides.

14. Sections or passages taken from a longer work, for example a book, film, musical composition, or document.

15. The parts created when something is split or separated into parts.

16. A basic unit of mass equal to 1,000 grams.

18. A book that consists of essays, stories, or poems by different writers.

19. To meet somebody or something, usually unexpectedly.

20. Things that have to be done so that something else can happen in the future.

Down

1. A bony, oily food fish of northern Atlantic coastal waters that has a greenish-blue body with dark blue bars and a forked tail.

3. A long-sleeved knitted jacket that fastens at the front.

4. A woman who rules an empire.

6. Disagreeing with somebody angrily.

7. A laundry, usually self-service, containing coin-operated washing and drying machines.

Down (continued)

8. The activity of shooting with a bow and arrow.

10. Stressing or giving importance to something.

11. A judge in a lower court.

12. Musical instruments with a long neck and usually six strings that are plucked or strummed.

13. Preparations that are applied to the face or the body to make it more attractive.

17. A large member of the cat family found mainly in Africa, and the fastest land mammal.

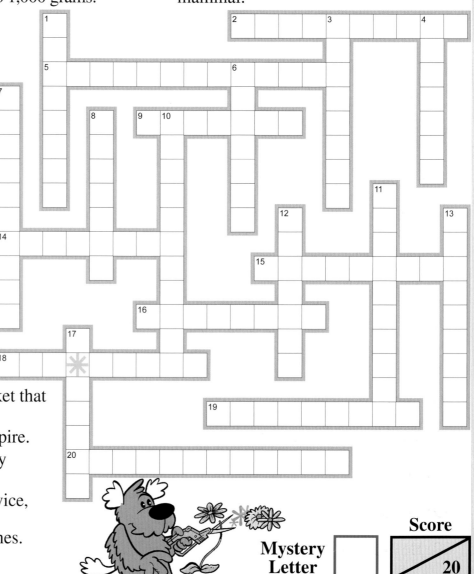

Mystery Letter

Score

20

excerpts	magistrate
arrangements	cheetah
divisions	cosmetics
mackerel	helicopter

Word Bank
TOTAL
3,920

Exercise 196a

1) Her tutor was always _____ the need to revise for exams.

2) She asked for a _____ of potatoes and the assistant weighed them for her.

3) _____ from the nominated films were shown before the winner was announced.

4) She rummaged through her make-up bag and checked her _____ .

5) The _____ 's speed, as it chased down its prey, reached over 100 km/h.

6) She enjoyed reading the _____ , with its diversity of authors.

7) My father and I went on a trip fishing for _____ off the coast of Cornwall.

8) The band's line-up comprised lead, rhythm and bass _____ , and drums.

9) The coastguard's _____ hovered over the ship ready to winch off survivors.

10) The case was heard in the local _____ 's court.

Score [/ 10]

Exercise 196b

11) She tried _____ for the first time and was surprised by the power of the bow.

12) "There's no point in _____ ; just do as you're told and go to bed!"

13) The _____ is named after the Earl who led the charge of the Light Brigade.

14) He takes his dirty washing to the _____ every Monday evening.

15) Deep _____ exist within the committee and consensus seems unlikely.

16) They had less than six weeks to finalise their wedding _____ .

17) The emperor died and his widow succeeded him as _____ .

18) The _____ worked with the dancers to perfect the routine.

19) The top, shaped like a _____ , was used like a die to generate numbers.

20) He expected to _____ many unforseen adversities.

Score [/ 10]

© 2006 Stephen Curran

lorgnette	exhilarating	crinoline
fashioned	ballerina	memorandum
excess	successor	motoring
hockey	evaporating	batted

Exercise 197a

1) "Don't be so _____ : show some respect for your elders!"

2) She raised the _____ to her eyes and studied the opera singer on stage.

3) She sent her manager a _____ to remind him of their appointment.

4) He _____ a chair from some leftover pieces of wood.

5) A Scotsman's _____ , that he wears in the top of his sock, is called a 'dirk'.

6) He was at the crease for over four hours and _____ magnificently.

7) The _____ drew in her arms and her pirouette increased in speed.

8) On his retirement, he introduced his _____ to the staff.

9) The _____ of her feet were sore after walking all day.

10) They tired of snooker and played _____ instead.   **Score** /10

Exercise 197b

11) _____ costs continue to escalate as petrol prices increase.

12) The sun is shining and the water in the puddles is _____ .

13) It was fashionable for Victorian women to wear a _____ under their skirts.

14) He drives a racing car and finds the danger and the speed _____ .

15) "Message understood, I'm _____ you loud and clear! Over!"

16) He struck the ball with his _____ , it hit the black, which went into the top pocket.

17) A *'pushback',* has replaced the *'bully-off'* at the start of a _____ match.

18) He enjoyed ballroom _____ , especially the waltz and the foxtrot.

19) She delved into her family's history in order to _____ the truth.

20) They checked in _____ baggage and had to pay extra.   **Score** /10

Word Bank

dagger	receiving
soles	dancing
cue	billiards
impertinent	uncover

Word Bank TOTAL 3,940

Across

197

1. An indoor game in which a felt-tipped cue is used to hit three coloured balls across a cloth-covered table into pockets.
6. Making somebody feel happy, excited, and more than usually vigorous and alive.
10. Changing a liquid into vapour, usually by heating to below its boiling point.
12. A stiff fabric made of horsehair and cotton or linen, used in the past for linings and petticoats.
14. A woman ballet dancer.
17. The amount by which one quantity exceeds another.
19. To find out about, or reveal something secret or previously hidden.
20. Somebody or something that follows another and takes up the same position.

Down

2. Picking up electronic signals and converting them into sound or pictures.
3. A note to serve as a reminder.
4. Gave shape or form to something.
5. Struck somebody or something with a bat.
7. Showing bold or rude lack of respect, especially to a superior.
8. Travelling by car or some other form of private vehicle.

Down (continued)

9. A pair of glasses or opera glasses with a short handle at the side.
11. Moving the feet and body rhythmically, usually in time to music.
13. A short, pointed knife used as a weapon.
15. A sport played between two teams of 11 players using sticks with curved ends and a ball.
16. A long tapering stick used to strike the cue ball in games such as billiards, snooker or pool.
18. The undersides of shoes or boots, sometimes excluding the heel.

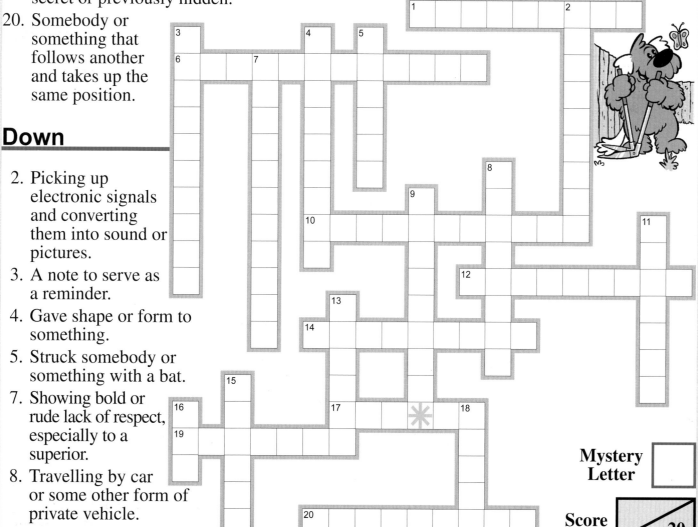

Mystery Letter

Score / 20

quickstep	neighbours	manageress
lyric	examinations	cooking
longbow	uneventful	bracelet
bowler	overalls	swivel

Across

198

1. Large, pink, wading birds native to tropical brackish waters.
3. A severe viral disease transmitted in the saliva of an infected animal.
10. The skill or practice of preparing food.
13. Not marked by any unusual or momentous occurrence.
14. To turn freely or horizontally in a circle.
16. A heavy jersey for leisure wear.
17. A piece of jewellery that is worn around the wrist.
18. A one piece protective garment with long sleeves and trousers.
19. Tests designed to assess somebody's ability or knowledge in a particular subject or field.

Down

2. A short poem expressing personal feelings or thoughts.
4. To move or walk unsteadily, almost but not quite falling over.
5. The component parts of a mixture, especially in cooking.
6. People who live, or are located, very close by.
7. The player who bowls the ball in cricket.
8. A hinged front part of a helmet designed to protect the eyes.
9. A large, powerful hand-drawn bow.
11. A female manager.
12. A ballroom dance with fast steps.
14. Something that stands for or represents something else.
15. A woman who brings food to tables, usually in a restaurant.

Don't forget to go back to page **18** and complete **Dickens's Mystery Word**. **!**

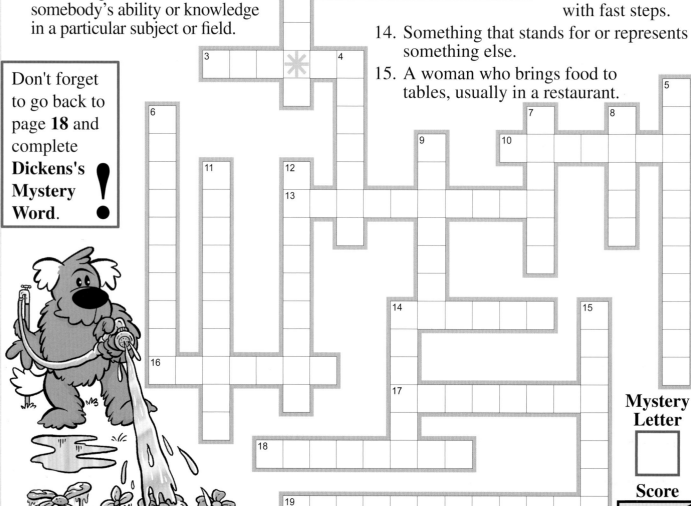

Mystery Letter

Score

20

sweater   visor
symbol   waitress
flamingoes   ingredients
rabies   stagger

Word Bank TOTAL 3,960

Exercise 198a

1) He is a _____ poet whose works portray poignant personal emotions.

2) She finished her workout and put on her _____ before she cooled down.

3) The _____ looked very graceful with their long legs and pinkish feathers.

4) They are extremely proficient ballroom dancers and excel at the _____ .

5) The _____ was a weapon feared by the armies of medieval England's enemies.

6) The English hatter, William _____ , designed his eponymous hat in 1850.

7) They enjoyed their meal and left a generous tip for the _____ .

8) Their new _____ called round to introduce themselves.

9) Quarantine regulations are designed to prevent the spread of _____ .

10) The mechanic's _____ were torn and oily.

Score [/ 10]

Exercise 198b

11) It had all the _____ of a great film and it was a box office smash.

12) The curry has been _____ for a while and smells delicious.

13) The day was boring and _____ with nothing much to report.

14) It was decided to _____ the start time for each class to avoid congestion.

15) "Fetch the _____ , I want to complain about her staff!"

16) She passed the _____ and qualified for admission.

17) He has a large desk with a high-backed _____ chair that rotates and reclines.

18) The letter 'V' made using the first two fingers is used as a _____ for victory.

19) She asked the jeweller to fit a safety chain to her _____ .

20) He pulled down the _____ before using the arc welder.

Score [/ 10]

Doing the Washing

Can you find all these words in the picture below? Write the correct word against each number. When you have finished you can colour in the picture if you want to.

clotheshorse	trousers	iron	cuff	pegs
washing machine	napkin	tea towel	detergent	buttons
ironing board	shirt	flex	T-shirt	laundry

1._____ 2._____ 3._____

4._____ 5._____ 6._____

7._____ 8._____ 9._____

10._____ 11._____ 12._____

13._____ 14._____ 15._____

© 2006 Stephen Curran

At the School Sports Day

Can you find all these words in the picture below? Write the correct word against each number.

baton	**trainer**	**javelin**	**medal**	**mattress**
timekeeper	**spectators**	**relay**	**high jump**	**lane**
judge	**winning post**	**long jump**	**stopwatch**	**winner**

1._____   2._____   3._____

4._____   5._____   6._____

7._____   8._____   9._____

10._____   11._____   12._____

13._____   14._____   15._____

orator   pane   outdoors
dandelion   boater   miser
recipe   vivacious   fitted
relief   unknown   objector

Across

199

3. Female police officers.
10. A female tiger.
11. A list of ingredients and instructions for making something.
12. A straw hat with a flat brim, a flat crown and a hat band.
14. Exhibiting or characterised by liveliness and high-spiritedness.
17. To have and be able to use something, especially power or authority.
18. Outside or in the open air.
19. Not forming part of somebody's knowledge or of knowledge in general.
20. Someone who is opposed to something, or expresses opposition to it.

Put the mystery letter (✳) into the box marked **199** below. Add in the mystery letters from puzzles **200** to **205** then rearrange them to make **Oliver's Mystery Word**.

The clue is **DRINKING VESSEL**.

Down

1. Evergreen trees or shrubs that have dark green needles and red cones that resemble berries.
2. A weed that has bright yellow flowers on a hollow stalk.
4. Somebody who gives speeches.
5. To put somebody or something in place of another, or to take the place of another.
6. A release from anxiety or tension.
7. A panel in front of the driver or pilot that contains indicator dials, switches and controls.
8. A glazed section of a window or door.
9. At a right angle to the horizon.
13. Tailored to fit closely to the body.
15. Taking hold of an object quickly and firmly.
16. Somebody who hoards money, hates spending it and, though rich, lives as if he or she were poor.

	199	200	201	202	203	204	205
Enter your mystery letters here:							

Mystery Word:

Now rearrange them:

Score ╱ 20

dashboard	substitute
seizing	policewomen
tigress	yews
wield	vertical

Exercise 199a

1) "We're going _____ . You'll need your hat and gloves."

2) He was a conscientious _____ and refused to fight in the war.

3) They forced entry into the house by breaking a window _____ in the back door.

4) A row of evergreen _____ lined the pathway to the ornamental pond and fountain.

5) She is a _____ old woman, always lively and full of vitality.

6) The next section of their ascent was almost _____ and was a real challenge.

7) _____ , like their male counterparts, begin their careers on the beat.

8) She picked the _____ , blew on its fluffy head and seeds flew into the air.

9) Large companies are able to _____ immense economic power.

10) Herb teas can be a pleasant _____ for coffee or tea.   **Score**   ⟋ 10

Exercise 199b

11) Although previously _____ , he was now becoming a household name.

12) He is a fine _____ and has been invited to make many after-dinner speeches.

13) The ground was muddy but the carriage's _____ protected the driver.

14) It is traditional to wear a rowing club blazer and straw _____ at the regatta.

15) Katherine, in *The Taming of the Shrew*, is a _____ with a fierce temper.

16) _____ the opportunity, he plucked up the courage to introduce himself.

17) "Don't be such a _____ ; spend some money and treat yourself for a change!"

18) She lost her child in the crowd and it was a great _____ to be reunited with him.

19) Their lack of planning and forethought was a _____ for disaster.

20) It appeared to be too small but it _____ her like a glove.   **Score**   ⟋ 10

summons	percolator	sandwiches
tidy	serviette	schooner
mechanic	alphabet	seashore
prance	auction	sue

Across

200

3. A fast sailing ship with at least two masts and with sails set lengthways.
5. To push somebody or something with great force.
6. To take legal action against somebody in order to obtain something, usually compensation for a wrong.
7. A written order to somebody to attend court to answer a complaint.
8. A set of letters, usually in a fixed order, used in writing a language.
12. A tiny opening in the skin through which substances, such as perspiration, can pass.
13. The sacred book of the Christian religion.

Across (continued)

14. A skilled worker who is employed to repair or operate machinery and engines.
16. A sale of goods or property at which buyers bid against one another for individual items.
17. The land lying next to the sea, especially a beach.
18. Slices of bread with a filling in between.

Down

1. A coffeepot.
2. A written daily record of personal experiences, rather more elaborate and detailed than a diary.
4. A police officer of the lowest rank.
7. A piece of cloth or tissue paper used at meal times to protect clothes and to wipe the mouth.
9. To move about in a lively and carefree, but often silly or annoying, way.
10. Having a neat orderly appearance.
11. An emotional or intellectual response that something arouses.
14. Somebody who owns and drives a car.
15. To raise or lift up somebody or something, especially using a mechanical device such as a winch.

Mystery Letter

Score

20

pore   journal

motorist   thrust

constable   hoist

Bible   reaction

Exercise 200a

1) She loved the sound of the _____ and the smell of fresh coffee.

2) He walked along the _____ looking for any interesting jetsam.

3) Her asthma was exacerbated by an allergic _____ to milk.

4) "May I pour you a large _____ of sherry before dinner?"

5) The Holy _____ contains the Scriptures of the Old and New Testaments.

6) She made her horse raise its front legs and _____ forward from its hind legs.

7) Both the _____ and the bearing had run dry and the shaft seized up.

8) She passed her exam and was promoted from police _____ to sergeant.

9) He retired to the library to _____ over another interesting book.

10) "The thieves made off with a _____ sum of money."   **Score** ⬚ **10**

Exercise 200b

11) The Cyrillic _____ is used in modern Slavonic languages.

12) The sailors pulled on the ropes in unison in order to _____ the sail.

13) The powerful _____ , generated by the rocket's engines, propelled it skywards.

14) She unfurled her _____ and placed it on her lap.

15) He was served with a _____ to appear in court.

16) He told the newspaper's publishers that he intended to _____ them for damages.

17) "Every _____ should leave their car at home and cycle to work!"

18) She asked the _____ to diagnose the problem and repair the engine.

19) He made cheese and pickle _____ to eat on the journey.

20) She bid the highest amount and won the _____ .   **Score** ⬚ **10**

chore	nectar	throb
sphere	carnation	punctually
mountainous	comic	nudge
concrete	skimmed	commerce

Exercise 201a

1) He wore a fresh, pink _____ in his lapel buttonhole every day.

2) The swan _____ across the surface before landing on the water.

3) His head continued to _____ so he took some paracetamol to relieve the pain.

4) "I'm prepared to listen if you have any _____ proposals."

5) "We're leaving at nine o'clock sharp, so be here _____ or we'll be gone!"

6) The success of the plan will _____ on the full cooperation of the whole team.

7) The bright orange _____ at Greenwich is known as the *'time-ball'*.

8) A computer is capable of processing vast amounts of _____ and analyzing the results.

9) _____ was the drink of the gods in Roman and Greek mythology.

10) The tyre marks were clearly _____ in the snow.

Score ☐ 10

Exercise 201b

11) Little John and _____ Tuck were members of Robin Hood's legendary band.

12) Some African tribes used rhythmic dancing to induce a _____ -like state.

13) She paused at the jeweller's shop and _____ the bracelet in the window.

14) He uses some of his pocket money to buy a _____ every week.

15) _____ is the central mechanism from which capitalism is derived.

16) She gave him a sharp _____ with her elbow when he began to snore.

17) His company _____ its customers with all manner of timber products.

18) The Roman *'fasces'* were used to _____ summary power and jurisdiction.

19) It is a very _____ region and inaccessible on foot.

20) "Homework can be a _____ but it has to be done!"

Score ☐ 10

ae

Across

201

1. Provided something that was wanted or needed by somebody.
2. So amusing that it induces smiles or laughter.
4. The large-scale buying and selling of goods and services.
6. A mixture of cement, sand, aggregate, and water that hardens to a strong stony consistency.
9. A perennial plant of the clove pink family with fringed petals.
12. Stated or described something clearly.
15. Removed the material accumulating on the surface of a liquid.
16. Any object similar in shape to a ball.
18. Arriving or taking place at the arranged time.

Down

1. To represent something by means of a symbol.
2. A task that is unpleasant, difficult, awkward, or boring to do.
3. Characterised by many mountains.
5. The sweet liquid that flowering plants produce.
7. To beat or pulsate in a rapid forceful way.
8. A hypnotic or cataleptic state.
10. Had a high opinion of somebody or something, for example a quality or attribute.
11. To push or poke somebody gently, usually with a motion of the elbow.
13. A man belonging to any of several Roman Catholic religious orders.
14. Information, often in the form of facts or figures, obtained from experiments or surveys.
17. A movable joint of metal or plastic used to fasten together two things, for example a box and its lid, and allow one of them to pivot.

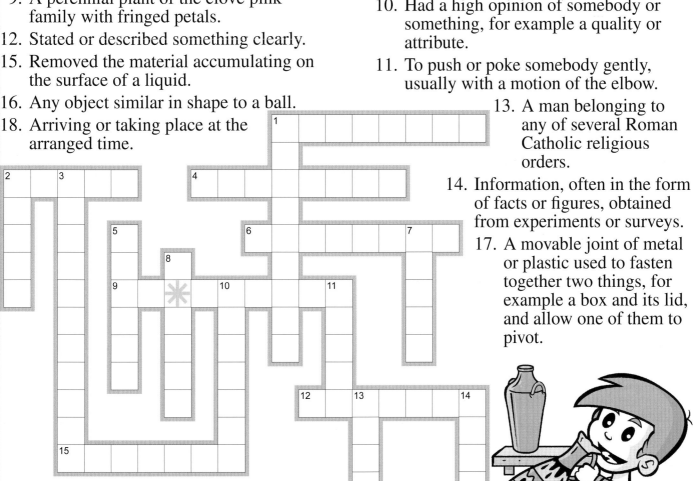

Score

Mystery Letter

20

43

blames **envying** **persuasion**
suffocates **hypnotise** **pregnant**
apologise **bilingual** **hopefully**
complicated **obviously** **nought**

Across

202

1. Considers somebody to be responsible for something wrong or unfortunate that has happened.
6. Used to suggest that there can be no doubt or uncertainty about something.
10. Exact and accurate, or detailed and specific.
13. The act of getting somebody to do or believe something.
14. An imaginary straight line around which an object, such as the Earth, rotates.
15. To put somebody into the sleep-like state of hypnosis.
17. Showing a lack of consideration for other people or for consequences.
19. To say you are sorry for something that has upset or inconvenienced somebody else.

Across (continued)

20. A place where somebody is hiding, especially someone wanted by the police.

Down

2. Desiring something possessed by somebody else.
3. Composed of many interrelated parts and therefore difficult to understand or deal with.
4. In a way that shows somebody's hope of having or receiving something.
5. Dies from lack of air.
7. Challenges openly somebody's or something's authority or power by refusing to obey a command or regulation.
8. Making a situation less tense, dangerous, or uncomfortable.
9. Able to speak two languages easily and naturally.
11. Carrying unborn offspring inside the body.
12. Gives the precise meaning of a word or expression.
16. The number zero.
18. A sound made when something soft and wet hits something hard.

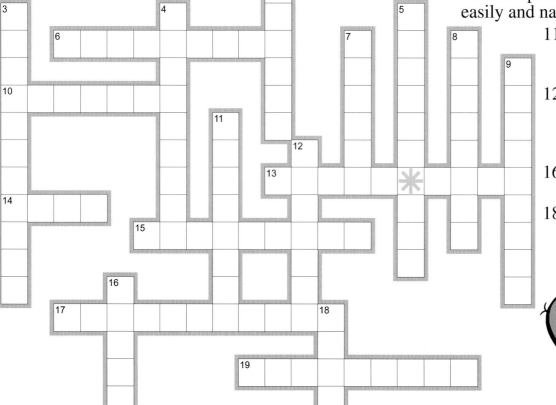

Mystery Letter

Score

20

hideout   **defies**

precise   **thoughtless**

splat   **axis**

defines   **defusing**

Word Bank
TOTAL
4,040

Exercise 202a

1) After a _____ pause, the boy said that he had not hurt the cat.

2) She was not of the same political _____ as her father.

3) The Earth's _____ is tilted at 23½ degrees relative to the ecliptic and points at Polaris.

4) The soldiers spent several hours _____ the bomb and rendering it harmless.

5) She is _____ and able to converse fluently in Spanish and English.

6) The instructions seemed _____ but he managed to follow them.

7) "It was _____ of you to act without consideration for others."

8) He swung a watch to and fro in front of her eyes in order to _____ her.

9) "The decision of the jury _____ all logic and disregards the evidence."

10) The wet fish landed in the bottom of the boat with a _____ .

Score / 10

Exercise 202b

11) He regretted his behaviour and wrote to _____ for his rudeness.

12) The police discovered the gang's _____ and recovered the stolen goods.

13) He found himself _____ their good fortune and wishing he could be as lucky.

14) At that _____ moment he entered the room and surprised them.

15) He was _____ hurt, though he tried not to show it.

16) Depriving a fire of oxygen _____ it and extinguishes the flames.

17) "She _____ you for the accident, although you deny all responsibility."

18) That row of trees _____ the northern boundary of the estate.

19) He added a _____ to one hundred to make it one thousand.

20) They listened _____ for the sound of the rescue party.

Score / 10

suspension	multiplying	completes
allocates	editorial	combined
whirr	litter	marries
claimant	revise	dries

Exercise 203a

1) The _____ weight of all the crew members is over 600 kilograms.

2) After such a dry winter, a summer _____ seems inevitable.

3) "Could you _____ your invoice and list every part and its cost."

4) The washing on the line _____ well when a warm wind blows strongly.

5) He is a talented player and is able to pass a long ball with _____ .

6) She placed the _____ between the pages and closed the book.

7) He was granted a last minute _____ and the execution was cancelled.

8) The terrain was extremely bumpy and the car's _____ was damaged.

9) There were five kittens in the _____ but only four survived.

10) He named himself as _____ on the insurance form. **Score** ⬛ /10

Exercise 203b

11) "If Dad _____ for a second time, we 'll have a stepmother."

12) He calculated the total cost, including 20% VAT, by _____ by 1.2.

13) He uses his men effectively and _____ a specific task to each one.

14) She heard the mechanism begin to _____ and the clock struck the hour.

15) The newspaper's _____ condemned the government's lack of action.

16) Every night after dinner, she went to her room to _____ for her exams.

17) He always spent his time _____ and did not waste it, unlike some of his friends.

18) The use of a bar code _____ speeds up transactions at shop checkouts.

19) She always _____ her work assignments on time.

20) He hoped to find a _____ job during the holidays. **Score** ⬛ /10

Word Bank

reader usefully
reprieve drought
bookmark casual
itemise precision

203

Across

3. In a manner that has some value or benefit, or serves some purpose.
4. Exactness or accuracy.
5. Somebody who brings a lawsuit against another person.
9. A long period of extremely dry weather when there is not enough rain for the successful growing of crops.
15. Somebody who reads or who reads in a particular manner.
16. Combines successfully.
18. To list all of a set of related things.
19. An article in a newspaper or magazine that expresses the opinion of its editor or publisher.
20. Makes something dry, or becomes dry.

Down

1. Joined or mixed together.
2. Shares out or divides something between a number of different people or projects.
6. Pieces of rubbish that have been carelessly left on the ground.
7. A strip of leather or other material inserted between the pages of a book to mark a place in it.
8. Performing the mathematical operation of multiplication.
10. An interruption of something for a period of time.
11. To halt or delay somebody's punishment.
12. Happening or done by chance or without prior thought or planning.
13. Reaches the normal and expected end.
14. To make a continuous soft buzzing or humming sound.
17. To come to different conclusions about somebody or something by thinking again.

Mystery Letter ☐

Score 　/20

47

vixen   reluctant   brightly
defining   impatient   previously
refuses   unlucky   blamed
device   Italy   radius

Across

204

3. Annoyed by being kept waiting or by being delayed.
5. A tool or machine designed to perform a particular task or function.
7. Declined to accept something offered.
11. Causing or heralding misfortune.
14. Not properly organised or ordered.
18. In a way that reflects or gives out a great deal of light.
19. Not needed or no longer needed.
20. A soft elastic mixture of flour and water that becomes bread or pastry when baked.

Down

1. A female fox.
2. Declares or makes known a decision or intention not to do something.
4. At an earlier time or on an earlier occasion.
6. A boot-shaped peninsula in the Mediterranean Sea.
8. Giving a distinctive character to something, or encapsulating its character.
9. Feeling no willingness or enthusiasm to do something.
10. A straight line extending from the centre of a circle to its edge.
12. In a manner that shows care, thoughtfulness, restraint and lack of haste.
13. A shy person who tends not to socialise much.
15. A speech sound other than a vowel.
16. Found fault with somebody.
17. A long, narrow, open container that holds feed or water for animals.

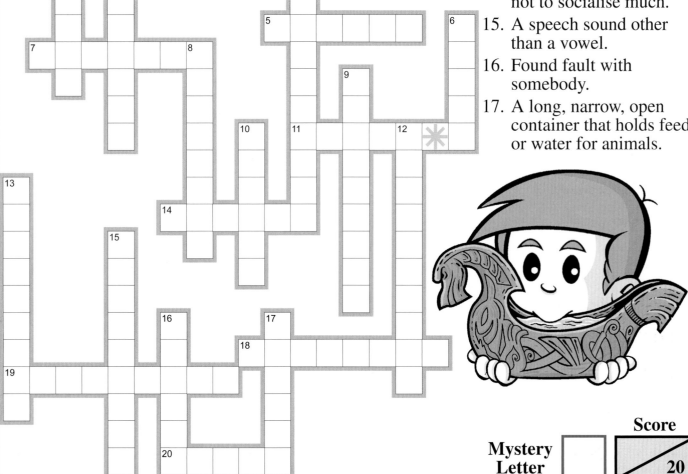

Mystery Letter

Score

/ 20

Exercise 204a

1) The baker put baking trays full of fresh _____ into the oven.

2) She had been here _____ and knew her way around.

3) They had kept him waiting for over an hour and he was growing _____ .

4) At dusk, we saw a fox, a _____ and their three cubs in the garden.

5) It is a splendid musical arrangement with rich, _____ , chords.

6) "A _____ of low pressure will move southwards during the day."

7) Although the sun was shining _____ , the air was still cold.

8) He used a length of rope as the _____ , attached it to a stake and scribed a circle.

9) Her friend is an _____ and prefers to stay in on her own.

10) No trip to _____ could be complete without seeing Venice.   **Score**   / 10

Exercise 204b

11) Many workers are made _____ by technological advances.

12) The 'Cat and Mouse Act' was introduced to deal with Suffragettes who _____ food.

13) Walking under a ladder is considered to be _____ by superstitious people.

14) That was the _____ speech in the election campaign and won him the seat.

15) She was _____ to drive through the night but she had to catch the ferry.

16) The supporters _____ the manager for the team's failure to avoid relegation.

17) "The road ahead is flooded: you should proceed _____ ," he warned.

18) If a horse _____ to jump an obstacle it incurs a penalty of four faults.

19) The room was _____ : his clothes were scattered everywhere.

20) A Geiger counter is a _____ used to detect radioactivity.   **Score**   / 10

allocated	outrageous	blaming
peacefully	sympathise	housewife
parallelogram	gurgle	caffeine
brood	perspire	tantalise

Exercise 205a

1) He would _____ the dog by repeatedly pretending to throw the ball.

2) The duck led her _____ of twelve ducklings down to the river.

3) They were each _____ a pillow, two sheets and two blankets.

4) The square, rectangle and rhombus are three special types of _____ .

5) The bath emptied with a loud _____ as the last of the water drained away.

6) The two sides entered into _____ in an attempt to resolve the dispute.

7) It was so humid that the slightest exertion made him _____ profusely.

8) The children had a choice of cola, _____ beer or lemonade to drink.

9) "I can _____ : the same thing happened to me last year."

10) She overslept and _____ to get washed and dressed.   **Score** ⬛ 10

Exercise 205b

11) With everyone profiteering from the shortages, the prices are _____ .

12) He expected to see the value of his house _____ over the next fifteen years.

13) She believed that her _____ was justified, so she complained to the manager.

14) She was a bored _____ , at home all day, looking for part-time work.

15) He decided to reduce his intake of _____ by drinking less coffee and tea.

16) The committee met to _____ a contingency plan to address the new threat.

17) "The breakdown in _____ harmony has made the situation tense."

18) Her baby was sleeping _____ , lulled by the gentle rocking motion.

19) He was always _____ someone else for his own failings.

20) It is difficult to _____ the exact meaning of some words.   **Score** ⬛ 10

50   © 2006 Stephen Curran ae

Word Bank
TOTAL
4,100

grievance	appreciate
ginger	dialogue
racial	devise
hurried	define

Across

2. A four-sided plane figure in which both pairs of opposite sides are parallel and of equal length and the opposite angles are equal.
4. Done, made, or performed too quickly because of a real or perceived lack of time.
7. Quietly, calmly and tranquilly.
9. Criticising somebody.
10. To be preoccupied with a troublesome or unwelcome thought.
12. Existing or taking place between different races.
15. A woman who does not go out to work but stays at home to manage the household.
16. To conceive of the idea for something and work out how to make it or put it into practice.
17. A widely-cultivated Asian plant with an edible underground stem.
18. To tease or torment people by letting them see, but not have, something they desire.
19. A stimulant found in coffee, tea, the cola nuts used to make soft drinks, and cocoa.
20. To secrete fluid from the sweat glands through the pores of the skin.

Down

1. To mark a boundary, edge, or limit.
3. To feel gratitude for something.
5. To share the feelings of somebody else or show pity or compassion for another.
6. To make a bubbling sound in the throat.
8. Given to a particular person or set aside for a particular purpose.
11. The words spoken by characters in a book, a film or a play.
13. Extravagant or unconventional, and likely to shock people.
14. A cause for complaint or resentment that may or may not be well-founded.

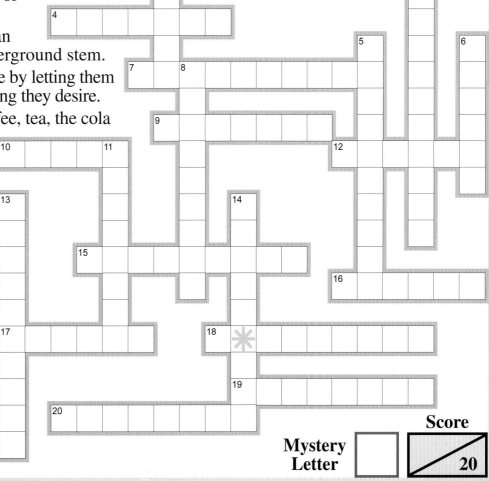

Don't forget to go back to page **38** and complete **Oliver's Mystery Word.**

Mystery Letter

Score / 20

Book Nine Word List

accept	blaming	concrete	discontent
accident	boater	confirm	divine
according	bookmark	connect	divisions
ache	bowler	connection	dodge
action	bracelet	consonant	dough
active	brightly	constable	dries
admired	brood	construct	drought
adopt	burglar	consume	dye
advise	bushel	contrast	editorial
allocated	cabin	contribute	either
allocates	caffeine	cooking	elbow
alphabet	cannon	cosmetics	emphasising
altitude	cardigan	costume	employ
angry	carnation	course	employer
anthology	casual	cricket	empress
apologise	cautiously	crinoline	enclose
appreciate	cellar	cruelly	encounter
archery	central	cruiser	entire
argue	centre	cue	entrance
arguing	century	cupboard	entry
argument	channel	current	envy
arrange	chapel	custom	envying
arrangements	cheetah	customer	errand
arranging	chimney	dagger	estate
arrest	chore	dancing	estimate
attempt	choreographer	dandelion	evaporating
attention	citizen	dashboard	evident
attract	claimant	data	examinations
auction	clerk	deceive	excellent
avenue	coax	decide	excerpts
axis	collect	defies	excess
balance	combined	define	excite
ballerina	comfortable	defined	exciting
bandage	comic	defines	exclaim
basin	command	defining	exclaimed
batted	commerce	defusing	exhilarating
beggar	common	department	expel
betray	compare	desert	explanation
beware	compel	device	exploration
Bible	complete	devise	explore
bilingual	completes	devour	fashion
billiards	complicated	dialogue	fashioned
blamed	compose	diamond	fertile
blames	concert	difficult	fever

Book Nine Word List

fitted	housewife	miser	policewomen
flamingoes	hurried	misery	population
flannel	hypnotise	moderate	pore
foreign	idea	monument	possess
fortunate	impertinent	motoring	practice
foundation	include	motorist	prance
frequent	ingredients	mountainous	precise
friar	inpatient	multiply	precision
fuel	insane	multiplying	pregnant
funnel	inspire	naked	prepare
further	introduce	nectar	preserve
gallery	introvert	neglect	previously
gentlemen	invade	neighbour	problem
ginger	invitation	neighbours	produce
glimpse	Italy	neither	progress
gospel	itemise	ninth	promise
government	jewel	nought	promote
grammar	journal	nudge	prompt
graze	junior	oath	punctually
grievance	justice	objector	purchase
grocer	kilogram	oblige	purpose
groceries	labour	observation	quickstep
growth	language	observe	rabies
guard	latitude	obviously	racial
guess	laundrette	onion	radius
guinea	lightning	orator	rapid
guitars	litter	outdoors	reaction
gulf	loan	outrageous	reader
gurgle	longbow	overalls	receive
habit	lorgnette	pane	receiving
happiness	lyric	parallelogram	recipe
harbour	mackerel	parcel	recite
headache	madam	passage	reduce
heathen	magic	pavement	redundant
height	magistrate	payment	refuge
helicopter	manageress	peacefully	refused
hexagon	marries	percolator	refuses
hideout	meanness	performance	reign
hinge	mechanic	perspire	relief
hockey	memorandum	persuasion	reluctant
hoist	mention	pigeon	represent
honour	mercy	pillar	reprieve
hopefully	minister	pledge	revise
hospital	minute	plunge	rogue

Book Nine Word List

ruin
sandwiches
satin
scarce
scare
scarf
schooner
scratch
seashore
seizing
sense
separate
service
serviette
shrink
situation
skimmed
slavery
sober
soles
speech
sphere

splat
sponge
stagger
straight
style
substance
substitute
successor
sue
suffocates
summons
supplied
supply
support
surpass
suspect
suspension
swear
sweater
swivel
symbol
symbolise

sympathise
tantalise
tempt
temptation
thirsty
thoughtless
throb
thrust
tidy
tigress
tongue
trance
trough
truly
tube
tune
turkey
umbrella
uncover
uneventful
unfortunate
unite

unknown
unlucky
untidy
usefully
valuable
vegetable
veil
vein
vertical
villain
violet
violin
visor
vivacious
vixen
waitress
whirr
wield
wrestle
wrist
written
yews

Congratulations!

You have now learnt to spell **4,100** words, know what they mean and how to use them in a sentence.

Now move on to **Book 10** to learn lots more words to add to your word bank total.

Answers

Exercise 184a
1) glimpse
2) Beware
3) action
4) coax
5) promise
6) sense
7) unfortunate
8) compare
9) loan
10) compose

Exercise 184b
11) estimate
12) betray
13) advise
14) active
15) oath
16) happiness
17) moderate
18) fortunate
19) preserve
20) prepare

Exercise 185a
1) burglar
2) wrestle
3) wrist
4) progress
5) turkey
6) costume
7) *Beggar*
8) pillar
9) tube
10) promote

Exercise 185b
11) written
12) heathen
13) produce
14) possess
15) cellar
16) tune
17) gentlemen
18) chimney
19) entire
20) grammar

Exercise 186a
1) represent
2) elbow
3) mention
4) grocer
5) discontent
6) attention
7) naked
8) evident
9) temptation
10) graze

Exercise 186b
11) situation
12) tempt
13) groceries
14) truly
15) speech
16) frequent
17) attempt
18) invitation
19) accident
20) growth

Crossword No. 184

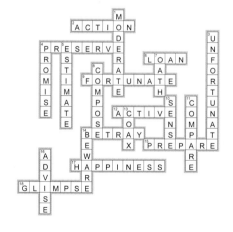

Crossword No. 185

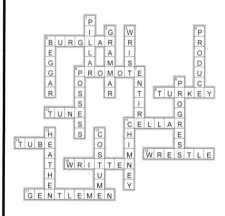

Crossword No. 186

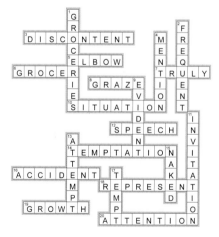

Letter = A

Letter = M

Letter = T

Answers

Exercise 187a
1) devour
2) rapid
3) harbour
4) gulf
5) plunge
6) satin
7) practice
8) sober
9) basin
10) service

Exercise 187b
11) population
12) cabin
13) habit
14) payment
15) justice
16) pigeon
17) according
18) labour
19) honour
20) accept

Exercise 188a
1) contribute
2) excellent
3) envy
4) explanation
5) exciting
6) oblige
7) contrast
8) exploration
9) expel
10) idea

Exercise 188b
11) exclaimed
12) excite
13) pavement
14) construct
15) consume
16) style
17) exclaim
18) angry
19) explore
20) confirm

Exercise 189a
1) compel
2) parcel
3) monument
4) gospel
5) bushel
6) jewel
7) reign
8) height
9) vein
10) veil

Exercise 189b
11) neighbour
12) swear
13) junior
14) chapel
15) either
16) course
17) foreign
18) language
19) department
20) Neither

Crossword No. 187

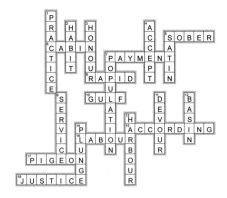

Letter = R

Crossword No. 188

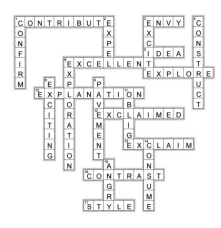

Letter = S

Crossword No. 189

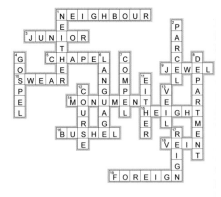

Letter = H

Exercise 190a

1) arrest
2) dye
3) madam
4) fuel
5) supply
6) entry
7) shrink
8) bandage
9) diamond
10) ruin

Exercise 190b

11) separate
12) enclose
13) government
14) magic
15) support
16) avenue
17) foundation
18) passage
19) cruelly
20) attract

Exercise 191a

1) latitude
2) observation
3) clerk
4) reduce
5) slavery
6) violin
7) onion
8) employer
9) customer
10) minute

Exercise 191b

11) fever
12) violet
13) misery
14) cricket
15) observe
16) employ
17) desert
18) custom
19) refuge
20) altitude

Exercise 192a

1) cruiser
2) difficult
3) arranging
4) funnel
5) neglect
6) connection
7) current
8) villain
9) umbrella
10) command

Exercise 192b

11) suspect
12) collect
13) gallery
14) cannon
15) connect
16) errand
17) channel
18) common
19) flannel
20) arrange

Crossword No. 190

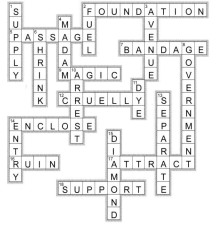

Letter = E

Crossword No. 191

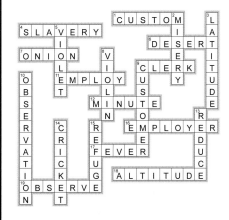

Letter = P

Crossword No. 192

Letter = S

At the Police Station

1. POSTER	2. EPAULETTE	3. PATROL CAR	4. NOTEBOOK	5. BATON
6. HANDCUFFS	7. CONSTABLE	8. WHISTLE	9. LAMP	10. RADIO
11. MOTORCYCLE	12. SERGEANT	13. KEY	14. HELMET	15. TORCH

At the Greengrocer's

1. SPRING BALANCE	2. SACK	3. CARROTS	4. PUNNET	5. SCALES
6. CONTAINER	7. BESOM	8. PRICE TAG	9. POTATOES	10. TRUG
11. APRON	12. MONEY BAG	13. MELON	14. UMBRELLA	15. AWNING

Answers

Exercise 193a

1) complete
2) scratch
3) hospital
4) argument
5) centre
6) minister
7) century
8) vegetable
9) deceive
10) valuable

Exercise 193b

11) surpass
12) citizen
13) further
14) estate
15) argue
16) comfortable
17) receive
18) central
19) purpose
20) purchase

Exercise 194a

1) headache
2) divine
3) substance
4) scarf
5) entrance
6) inspire
7) insane
8) meanness
9) performance
10) straight

Exercise 194b

11) lightning
12) scare
13) dodge
14) include
15) ache
16) invade
17) pledge
18) introduce
19) balance
20) scarce

Oliver's Page of Knowledge

1. Pantechnicon *Ramp.*

2. Freighter *Derrick.*

3. Skiff *Rowlock.*

4. Steam Engine *Tender.*

5. Aeroplane *Rudder.*

6. Helicopter *Rotor.*

7. Hovercraft *Skirt.*

8. Galleon *Rigging.*

9. Bicycle *Chain.*

10. Airboat *Propeller.*

Crossword No. 193

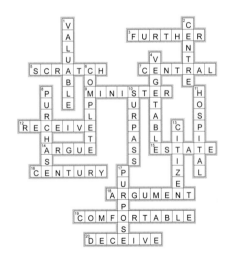

Letter = P

Crossword No. 194

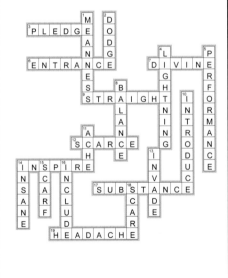

Letter = E

Answers

Exercise 195a
1) thirsty
2) rogue
3) guard
4) concert
5) fertile
6) fashion
7) guess
8) guinea
9) prompt
10) multiply

Exercise 195b
11) sponge
12) decide
13) recite
14) unite
15) cupboard
16) ninth
17) problem
18) adopt
19) mercy
20) tongue

Exercise 196a
1) emphasising
2) kilogram
3) Excerpts
4) cosmetics
5) cheetah
6) anthology
7) mackerel
8) guitars
9) helicopter
10) magistrate

Exercise 196b
11) archery
12) arguing
13) cardigan
14) launderette
15) divisions
16) arrangements
17) empress
18) choreographer
19) hexagon
20) encounter

Exercise 197
1) impertinent
2) lorgnette
3) memorandum
4) fashioned
5) dagger
6) batted
7) ballerina
8) successor
9) soles
10) billiards

Exercise 197
11) Motoring
12) evaporating
13) crinoline
14) exhilarating
15) receiving
16) cue
17) hockey
18) dancing
19) uncover
20) excess

Crossword No. 195
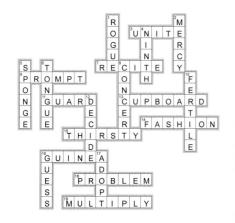

Letter = O

Crossword No. 196
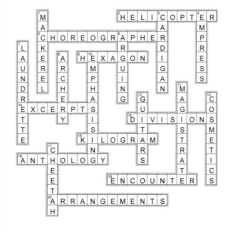

Letter = H

Crossword No. 197
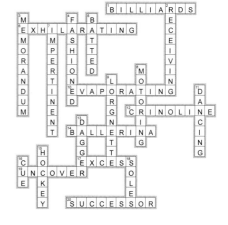

Letter = E

Doing the Washing

1. IRONING BOARD	2. T-SHIRT	3. NAPKIN	4. PEGS	5. FLEX
6. LAUNDRY	7. SHIRT	8. CUFF	9. BUTTONS	10. TROUSERS
11. CLOTHESHORSE	12. WASHING MACHINE	13. TEA TOWEL	14. IRON	15. DETERGENT

At the School Sports Day

1. MEDAL	2. LANE	3. MATTRESS	4. HIGH JUMP	5. JAVELIN
6. LONG JUMP	7. RELAY	8. WINNER	9. STOPWATCH	10. JUDGE
11. TRAINER	12. WINNING POST	13. BATON	14. TIMEKEEPER	15. SPECTATORS

Answers

Exercise 198a
1) lyric
2) sweater
3) flamingoes
4) quickstep
5) longbow
6) Bowler
7) waitress
8) neighbours
9) rabies
10) overalls

Exercise 198b
11) ingredients
12) cooking
13) uneventful
14) stagger
15) manageress
16) examinations
17) swivel
18) symbol
19) bracelet
20) visor

Exercise 199a
1) outdoors
2) objector
3) pane
4) yews
5) vivacious
6) vertical
7) Policewomen
8) dandelion
9) wield
10) substitute

Exercise 199b
11) unknown
12) orator
13) dashboard
14) boater
15) tigress
16) Seizing
17) miser
18) relief
19) recipe
20) fitted

Exercise 200a
1) percolator
2) seashore
3) reaction
4) schooner
5) Bible
6) prance
7) journal
8) constable
9) pore
10) tidy

Exercise 200b
11) alphabet
12) hoist
13) thrust
14) serviette
15) summons
16) sue
17) motorist
18) mechanic
19) sandwiches
20) auction

Crossword No. 198

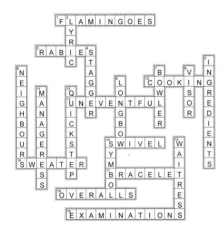

Letter = I

Crossword No. 199

Letter = D

Crossword No. 200

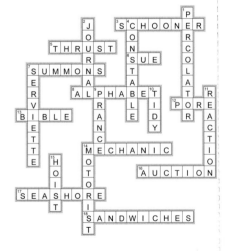

Letter = N

© 2006 Stephen Curran

Exercise 201a

1) carnation
2) skimmed
3) throb
4) concrete
5) punctually
6) hinge
7) sphere
8) data
9) Nectar
10) defined

Exercise 201b

11) Friar
12) trance
13) admired
14) comic
15) Commerce
16) nudge
17) supplied
18) symbolise
19) mountainous
20) chore

Exercise 202a

1) pregnant
2) persuasion
3) axis
4) defusing
5) bilingual
6) complicated
7) thoughtless
8) hypnotise
9) defies
10) splat

Exercise 202b

11) apologise
12) hideout
13) envying
14) precise
15) obviously
16) suffocates
17) blames
18) defines
19) nought
20) hopefully

Exercise 203a

1) combined
2) drought
3) itemise
4) dries
5) precision
6) bookmark
7) reprieve
8) suspension
9) litter
10) claimant

Exercise 203b

11) marries
12) multiplying
13) allocates
14) whirr
15) editorial
16) revise
17) usefully
18) reader
19) completes
20) casual

Crossword No. 201

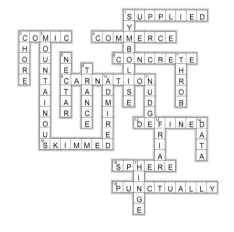

Crossword No. 202

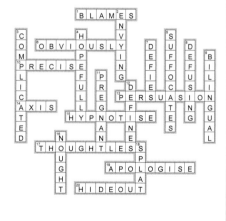

Crossword No. 203

Letter = R

Letter = A

Letter = T

Answers

Exercise 204a

1) dough
2) previously
3) impatient
4) vixen
5) consonant
6) trough
7) brightly
8) radius
9) introvert
10) Italy

Exercise 204b

11) redundant
12) refused
13) unlucky
14) defining
15) reluctant
16) blamed
17) cautiously
18) refuses
19) untidy
20) device

Exercise 205a

1) tantalise
2) brood
3) allocated
4) parallelogram
5) gurgle
6) dialogue
7) perspire
8) ginger
9) sympathise
10) hurried

Exercise 205b

11) outrageous
12) appreciate
13) grievance
14) housewife
15) caffeine
16) devise
17) racial
18) peacefully
19) blaming
20) define

Crossword No. 204

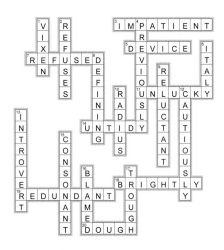

Letter = K

Crossword No. 205

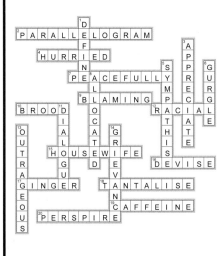

Letter = A

Mystery Word
A M T R S H E
H A M S T E R

Mystery Word
P S P E O H E I
H O S E P I P E

Mystery Word
D N R A T K A
T A N K A R D

PROGRESS CHARTS

Scores

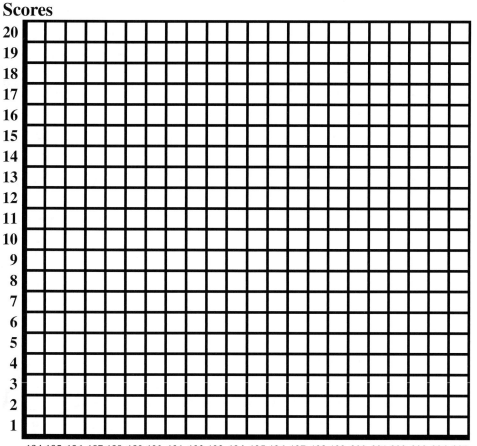

Exercises

Shade in your score for each exercise on the graph. Add them up for your total score out of 460. Ask an adult to work out the percentage.

Total Score

Percentage

 A

Scores

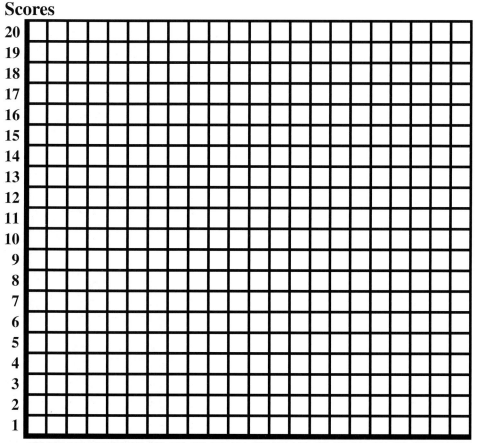

Crosswords

Shade in your score for each crossword on the graph. Add them up for your total score out of 460.

Total Score

Percentage

 B

For the average percentage add %A and %B and divide by 2

Overall Percentage

%

CERTIFICATE OF

ACHIEVEMENT

This certifies

_____

has successfully completed

11+ Spelling & Vocabulary

WORKBOOK **9**

Overall percentage
score achieved

%

Comment _____

_____

Signed _____

(teacher/parent/guardian)

Date _____